Painting

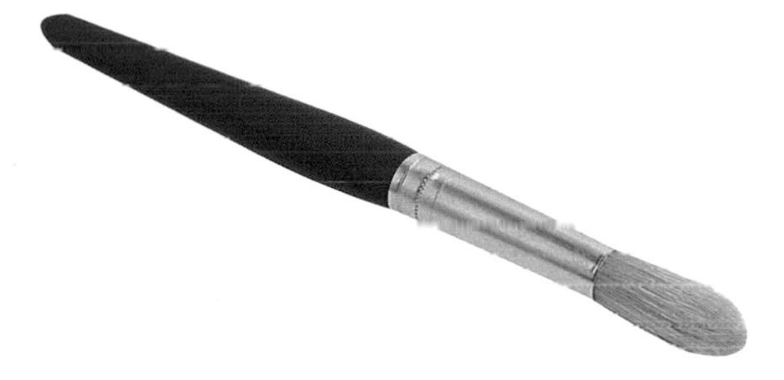

Written by Julie Ellis
Photography by Michael Curtain

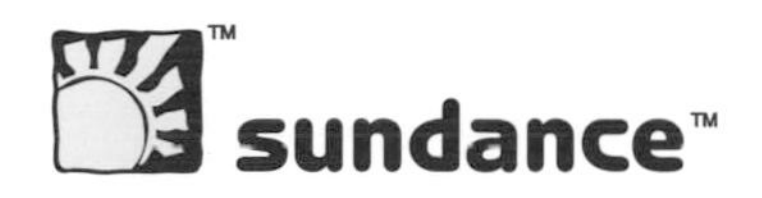

Look at me.
I can paint
with a paintbrush.

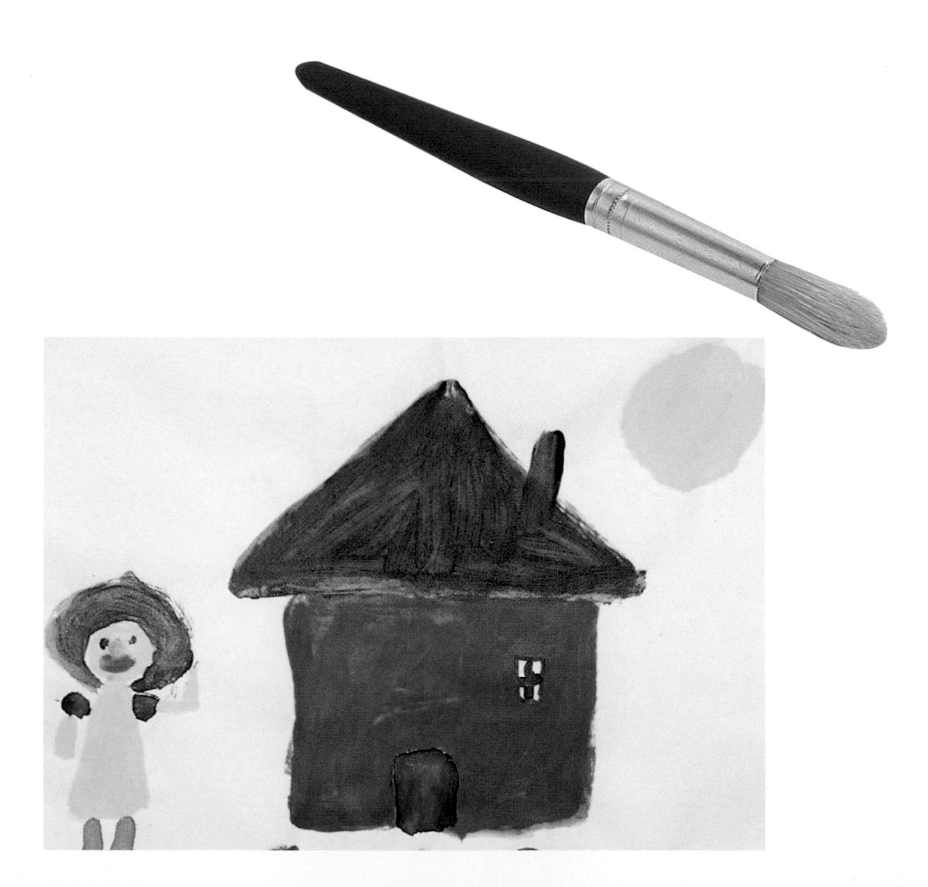

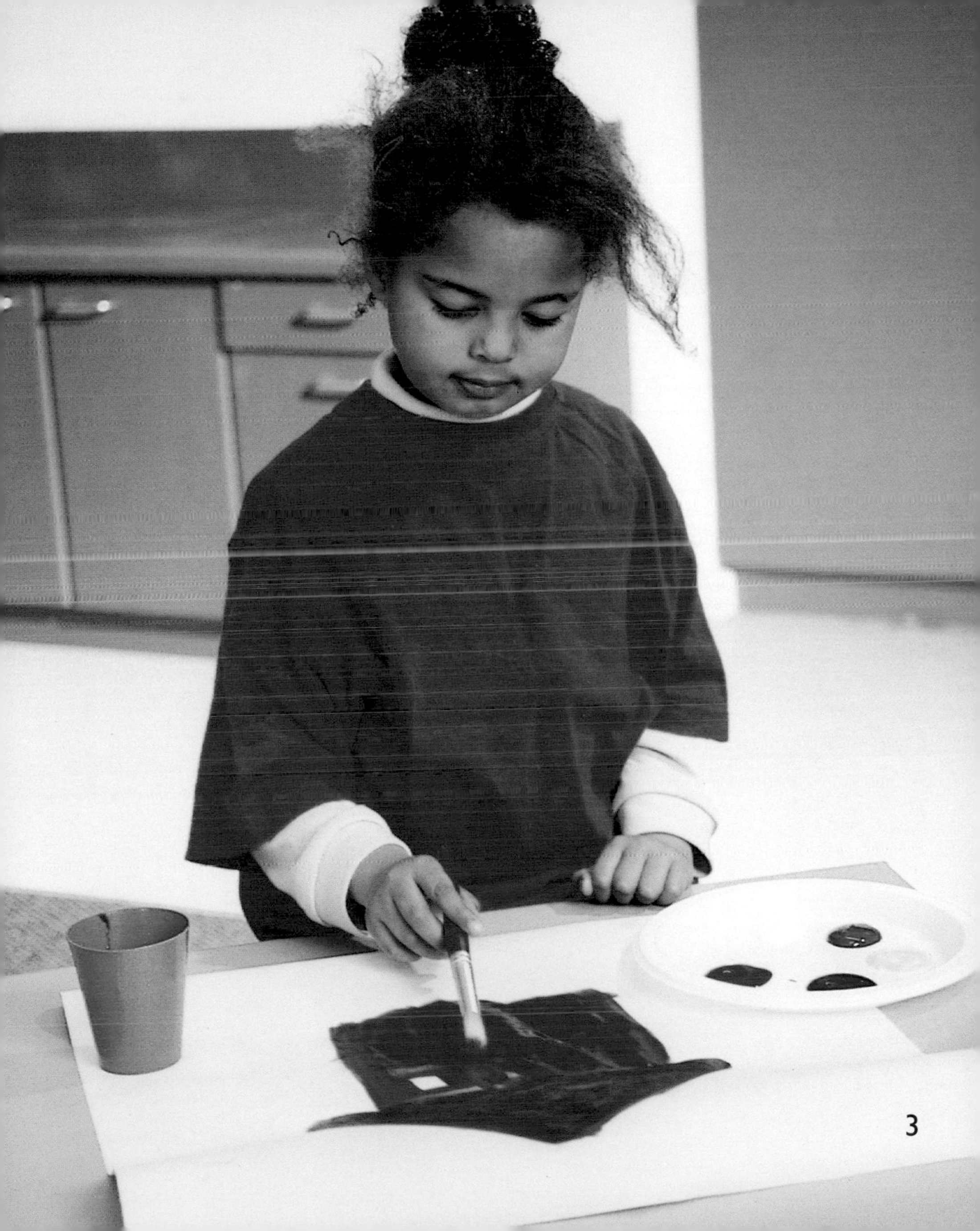

Look at me.
I can paint
with a straw.

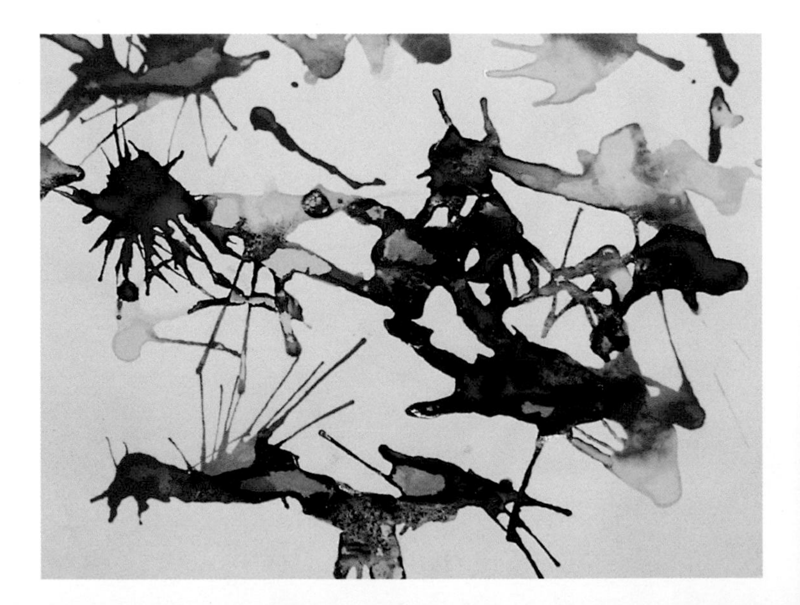

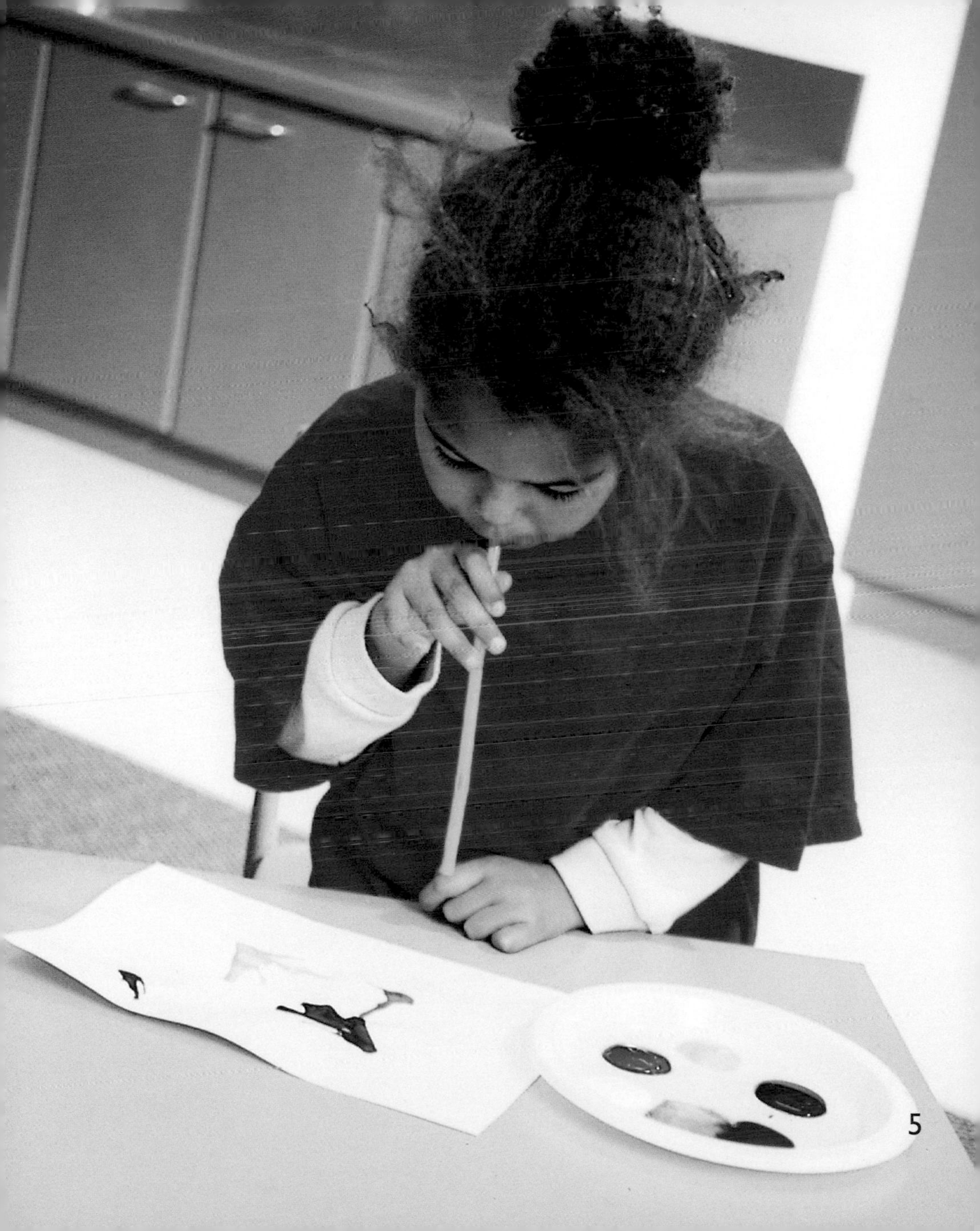

Look at me.
I can paint
with a toothbrush.

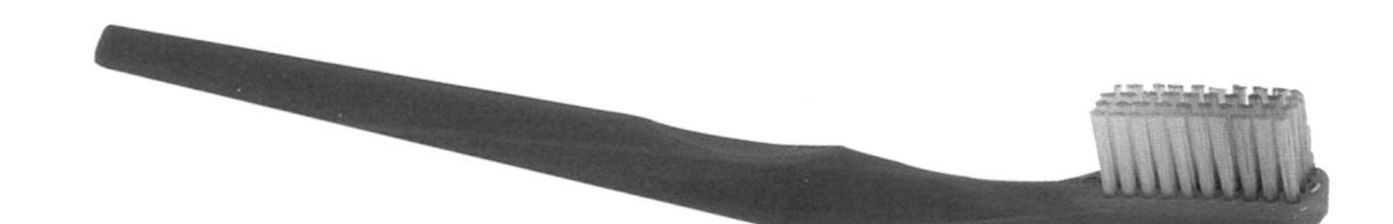

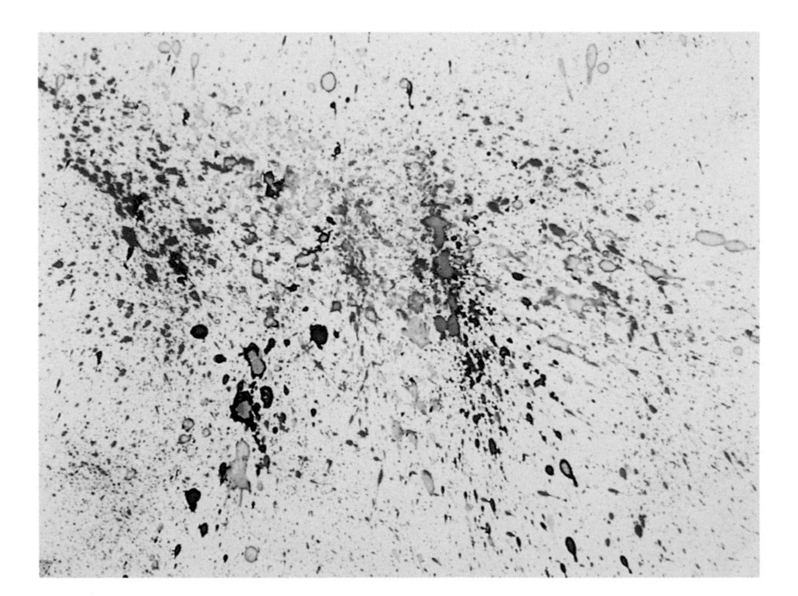

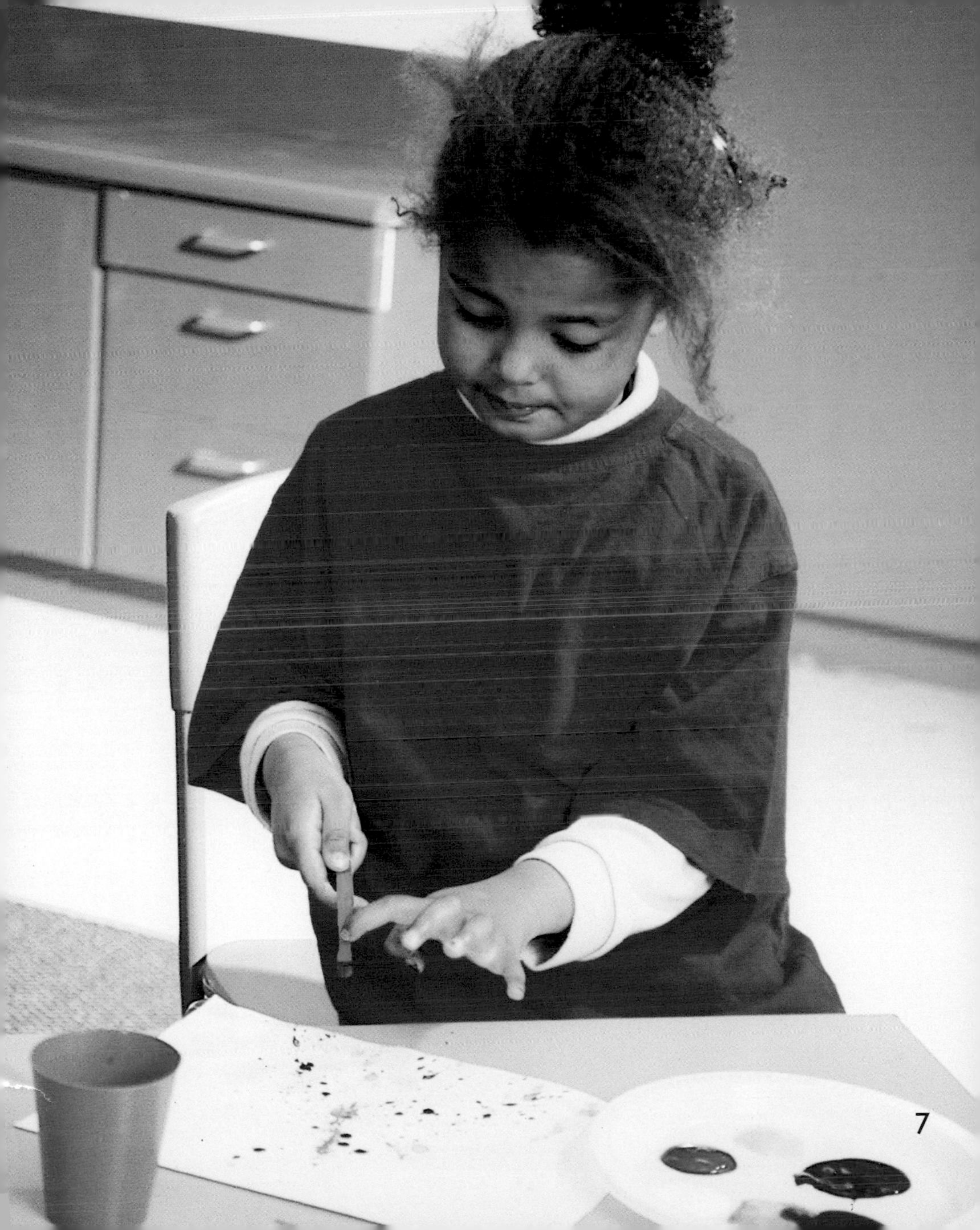

Look at me.
I can paint
with a roller.

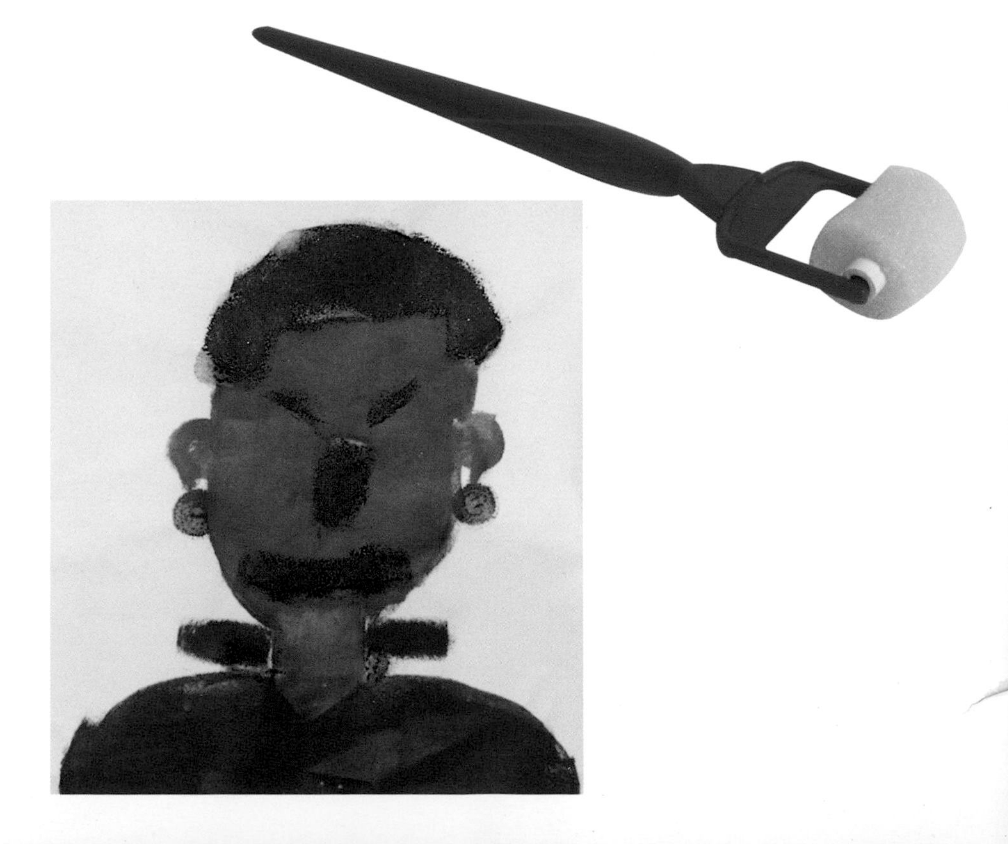